Intermediate 1 | Units 1, 2 & 3
Mathematics

Leckie×Leckie

First exam published in 2001.

Published by Leckie & Leckie, 8 Whitehill Terrace, St. Andrews, Scotland KY16 8RN tel: 01334 475656 fax: 01334 477392 enquiries@leckieandleckie.co.uk www.leckieandleckie.co.uk

Leckie & Leckie Project Team: Andrea Collington; Peter Dennis; Bruce Ryan

ISBN 1-84372-217-8

A CIP Catalogue record for this book is available from the British Library.

Printed in Scotland by Scotprint.

Leckie & Leckie is a division of Granada Learning Limited, part of ITV plc.

Acknowledgements

Every effort has been made to trace the copyright holders and to obtain their permission for the use of copyright material.
Leckie & Leckie will gladly receive information enabling them to rectify any error or omission in subsequent editions.

INTERMEDIATE 1

SPECIMEN QUESTION PAPER

FOR OFFICIAL USE

Total mark

X100/101

NATIONAL
QUALIFICATIONS

Time: 35 minutes

SPECIMEN QUESTION PAPER

**MATHEMATICS
INTERMEDIATE 1
Units 1, 2 and 3
Paper 1
(Non-calculator)**

Fill in these boxes and read what is printed below.

Full name of centre

Town

Forename(s)

Surname

Date of birth
Day Month Year

Scottish candidate number

Number of seat

1 **You may NOT use a calculator.**

2 Write your working and answers in the spaces provided. Additional space is provided at the end of this question-answer book for use if required. If you use this space, write clearly the number of the question involved.

3 Full credit will be given only where the solution contains appropriate working.

4 Before leaving the examination room you must give this book to the invigilator. If you do not you may lose all the marks for this paper.

SCOTTISH
QUALIFICATIONS
AUTHORITY

FORMULAE LIST

Circumference of a circle: $C = \pi d$
Area of a circle: $A = \pi r^2$

Theorem of Pythagoras:

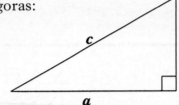

$a^2 + b^2 = c^2$

Trigonometric ratios
in a right angled
triangle:

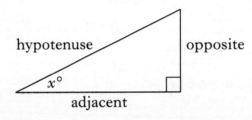

$$\tan x^\circ = \frac{\text{opposite}}{\text{adjacent}}$$

$$\sin x^\circ = \frac{\text{opposite}}{\text{hypotenuse}}$$

$$\cos x^\circ = \frac{\text{adjacent}}{\text{hypotenuse}}$$

Marks

ALL questions should be attempted.

1. (*a*) Find $\frac{5}{6}$ of 114.

1

   (*b*) Find 30% of £240.

1

2. When Douglas went to Belgium the exchange rate was 1·53 euros to the pound. How many euros did he get for £200?

2

[Turn over

Marks

3. Amy records the number of letters per word in the first hundred words in a book.

The results are shown in this frequency table.

Number of letters per word	Frequency
1	2
2	18
3	21
4	20
5	9
6	7
7	7
8	4
9	8
10	1
11	1
12	2
	Total = 100

(a) Find the median number of letters per word.

1

(b) Find the probability that a word contains five letters.

1

Marks

4. The table shows the populations of five Scottish towns in 2001.

TOWN	POPULATION (to the nearest 10 000)
Aberdeen	190 000
Dundee	170 000
Edinburgh	420 000
Kirkcaldy	50 000
Paisley	80 000

On the grid below, draw a bar graph to show this information.

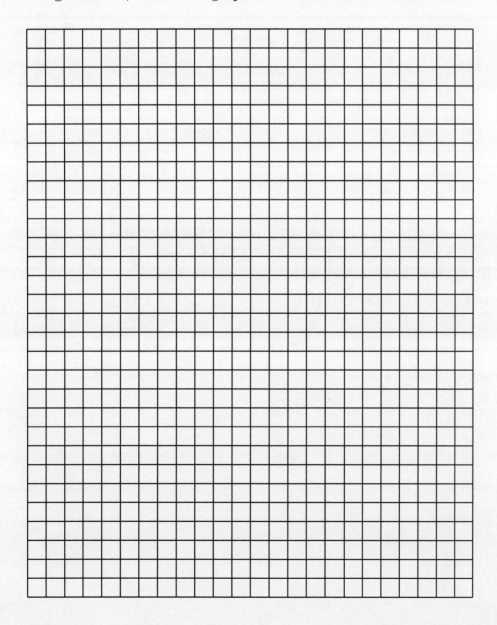

4

[Turn over

Marks

5. RM Enterprises make guttering for draining liquid.

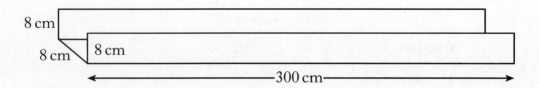

8 cm

8 cm   8 cm

←————————————300 cm————————————→

Assuming that end pieces are fitted, what volume of liquid will this section of guttering hold when completely full?

2

6. An employee wants to take out a pension plan. He is told that when he retires he will receive an annual pension of £150 for every £1000 he has invested. By the time he retires he should have invested £42 000.

What annual pension should he receive?

2

Marks

7. Solve algebraically the equation

$$6a - 5 = 17 + 2a.$$

3

[Turn over

Marks

8. (*a*) Complete the table below for $y = 1 - 2x$.

x	-2	0	5
y	5	1	-9

2

(*b*) Draw the line $y = 1 - 2x$ on the grid.

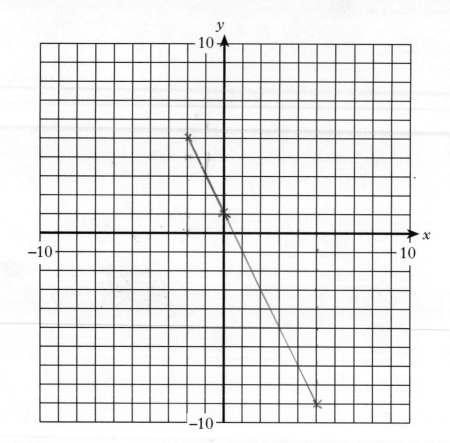

2

Marks

9. During one week in winter, the midday temperatures in Oban were as shown.

Sunday	−1 °C
Monday	−2 °C
Tuesday	−3 °C
Wednesday	−4 °C
Thursday	2 °C
Friday	0 °C
Saturday	1 °C

(*a*) Calculate the mean of these temperatures.

3

(*b*) Calculate the range of these temperatures.

2

[Turn over

Marks

10. The graph shows the speed of a holiday liner as it sailed from one port to another.

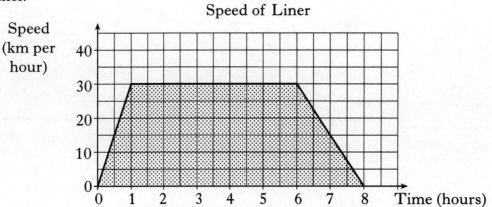

(*a*) The graph shows that during the first hour the liner increased speed from 0 to 30 km per hour.

Describe the speed of the boat over the remainder of the journey.

2

Marks

10. (continued)

When we have a graph of speed against time, the **area under the graph** tells us the total distance travelled.

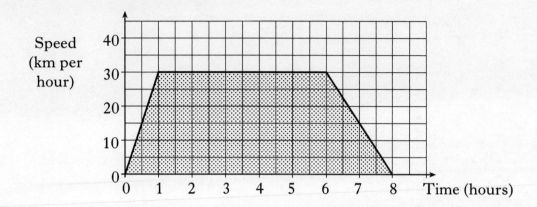

(*b*) By calculating the shaded area above, find the total distance travelled by the liner.

4

[END OF QUESTION PAPER]

Page eleven

ADDITIONAL SPACE FOR ANSWERS

FOR OFFICIAL USE

Total
mark

X100/103

NATIONAL
QUALIFICATIONS

Time: 55 minutes

SPECIMEN QUESTION PAPER

MATHEMATICS
INTERMEDIATE 1
Units 1, 2 and 3
Paper 2

Fill in these boxes and read what is printed below.

Full name of centre

Town

Forename(s)

Surname

Date of birth
Day Month Year   Scottish candidate number   Number of seat

1   **You may use a calculator.**

2   Write your working and answers in the spaces provided. Additional space is provided at the end of this question-answer book for use if required. If you use this space, write clearly the number of the question involved.

3   Full credit will be given only where the solution contains appropriate working.

4   Before leaving the examination room you must give this book to the invigilator. If you do not you may lose all the marks for this paper.

SCOTTISH
QUALIFICATIONS
AUTHORITY

FORMULAE LIST

Circumference of a circle: $C = \pi d$
Area of a circle: $A = \pi r^2$

Theorem of Pythagoras:

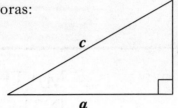

$a^2 + b^2 = c^2$

Trigonometric ratios
in a right angled
triangle:

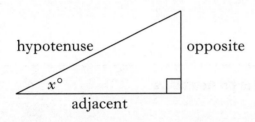

$$\tan x° = \frac{\text{opposite}}{\text{adjacent}}$$

$$\sin x° = \frac{\text{opposite}}{\text{hypotenuse}}$$

$$\cos x° = \frac{\text{adjacent}}{\text{hypotenuse}}$$

Marks

ALL questions should be attempted.

1.   Mary has a recipe for making fairy cakes.

         150 g flour
         100 g sugar
         100 g margarine
         2 eggs

This recipe makes 12 cakes.

Mary has promised to make 30 cakes for the office party.

How much sugar will she need?

2

2.   A dairy produces $2 \cdot 3 \times 10^9$ litres of milk per day.

Calculate the number of litres produced per week.

Give your answer in standard form.

2

[Turn over

Marks

3. Jean wants to take £40 out of her bank account. In the bank she is offered £5 notes, £10 notes or £20 notes. Jean decides that she will take four £5 notes and two £10 notes.

Find as many different ways as you can to make up the £40 using £5, £10 or £20 notes.

Show your answers in the table given.

	£5 notes	£10 notes	£20 notes
Jean's choice	4	2	0

4

Marks

4. 564 items were borrowed from a music library during one week.

The pie chart below shows the different types of items borrowed.

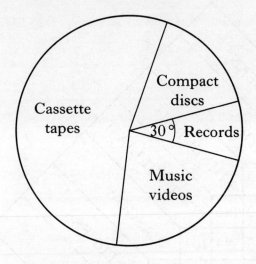

How many records were borrowed that week?

3

[Turn over

Marks

5. The table below shows the distances in miles between different places in Scotland.

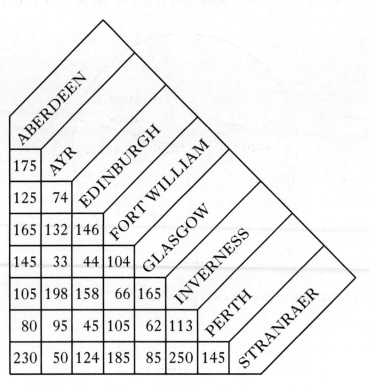

(a) Use the table to find the distance from Ayr to Inverness.

1

(b) Donna is in Ayr and is planning to drive to Inverness.
   She can travel at an average speed of 45 miles per hour.
   How long should her journey take, in hours and minutes?

3

Marks

6. (*a*) Multiply out the brackets and simplify

$$2(7a - 3b) + 5b.$$

$14a - 6b + 5b$

$14a - 1b$

2

(*b*) Factorise $5x - 20.$

$5(x - 4)$

2

7. Solve algebraically the inequality

$$3y - 6 \geq 12.$$

$3y \geq 12 + 6$

$3y \geq 18$

$y \geq \dfrac{18}{3}$

$y \geq 6$

2

[Turn over

Page seven

Marks

8. The size of a television screen is given by the length of the diagonal line from one corner of the screen to the opposite corner.

   This is a **14 inch** screen.

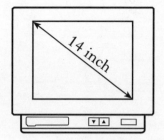

   Calculate the size of this rectangular television screen.

   Give your answer correct to one decimal place.

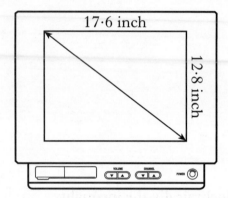

   Do not use a scale drawing.

4

Marks

9. Alison has invested £16 000 in a bank account which pays 6·5% interest per annum.

   She invests the money for 3 months.

   Calculate the interest she receives on her money.

   3

10. A plane taking off from Prestwick Airport rises at an angle of 25° to the ground.

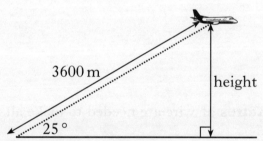

   3600 m

   height

   25°

   Find the height of the plane after it has travelled 3600 metres.

   Give your answer correct to the nearest hundred metres.

   Do not use a scale drawing.

   4

   [Turn over

DO NOT
WRITE IN
THIS
MARGIN

Marks

11. The edging for a garden path is made from metal wire.

The wire is bent to form semi-circular loops as shown below.

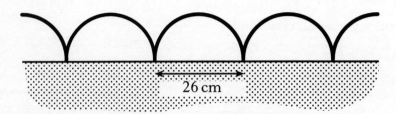

26 cm

Each loop is 26 centimetres across.

(*a*) Find the number of loops needed for one side of a path 13 metres long.

2

(*b*) How many **whole metres** of wire are needed to make all the loops for one side of this path?

4

Marks

12. In 1990, a school had 1050 pupils.

By 2000, the number of pupils had fallen by 126.

Calculate the percentage decrease in the number of pupils.

3

[Turn over for Question 13 on Page twelve

Page eleven

Marks

13. The time taken, T seconds, by a child to slide down a chute of length ℓ metres and height h metres is given by formula

$$T = \frac{5\ell}{\sqrt{h}}$$

(a) Calculate T when the length is 2·4 metres and the height 1·44 metres.

3

(b) It takes 15 seconds for a child to slide down a chute of height 2·56 metres.

Find the length of the chute.

2

[END OF QUESTION PAPER]

INTERMEDIATE 1 2001

Official SQA Past Papers: Intermediate 1 Mathematics 2001

FOR OFFICIAL USE

Total mark

X056/101

NATIONAL
QUALIFICATIONS
2001

THURSDAY, 17 MAY
9.00 AM – 9.35 AM

MATHEMATICS
INTERMEDIATE 1
Units 1, 2 and 3
Paper 1
(Non-calculator)

Fill in these boxes and read what is printed below.

Full name of centre

Town

Forename(s)

Surname

Date of birth
Day Month Year   Scottish candidate number   Number of seat

1 You may **NOT** use a calculator.

2 Write your working and answers in the spaces provided. Additional space is provided at the end of this question-answer book for use if required. If you use this space, write clearly the number of the question involved.

3 Full credit will be given only where the solution contains appropriate working.

4 Before leaving the examination room you must give this book to the invigilator. If you do not you may lose all the marks for this paper.

SCOTTISH
QUALIFICATIONS
AUTHORITY

LIB X056/101 6/12270

FORMULAE LIST

Circumference of a circle: $C = \pi d$

Area of a circle: $A = \pi r^2$

Theorem of Pythagoras:

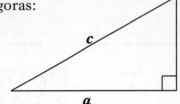

$a^2 + b^2 = c^2$

Trigonometric ratios
in a right angled
triangle:

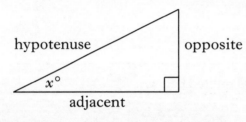

$\tan x° = \dfrac{\text{opposite}}{\text{adjacent}}$

$\sin x° = \dfrac{\text{opposite}}{\text{hypotenuse}}$

$\cos x° = \dfrac{\text{adjacent}}{\text{hypotenuse}}$

Marks

ALL questions should be attempted.

1. (*a*) Find $7·35 \times 8$.

1

(*b*) Find $\frac{3}{4}$ of £82.

1

2. Part of the timetable of the overnight bus from Stirling to London is shown opposite.

| Stirling (depart) | 2140 |
| London (arrive) | 0615 |

How long does the journey from Stirling to London take?

1

3. Eight jars of jam can be made from 2 kilograms of raspberries.
How many jars of jam can be made from 5 kilograms of raspberries?

2

[Turn over

Marks

4. Jenna is buying a car. The cash price is £11 500. It can be bought on hire purchase by paying a deposit of 20% of the cash price and 36 instalments of £300.

    Find the total hire purchase price of the car.

3

5. Solve algebraically the equation

    $$7b - 6 = 3b + 38.$$

3

Marks

6. During a period of 30 days the temperature at a weather station is recorded each day.

   The frequency table below shows these temperatures.

Temperature (°C)	Frequency	Temperature × Frequency
−3	1	
−2	2	
−1	4	
0	2	
+1	6	
+2	8	
+3	3	
+4	4	

(a) Write down the modal temperature.

1

(b) Complete the table above and find the mean temperature.
    Give your answer as a decimal.

3

[Turn over

Marks

7. (a) Multiply out the brackets and simplify

$$8w + 3(2 - w).$$

2

(b) Factorise $\quad 45 + 5a.$

2

Marks

8. (*a*) Complete the table below for $y = 2x - 5$.

x	−1	0	4
y			

2

(*b*) Using the table in part (*a*), draw the graph of $y = 2x - 5$ on the grid.

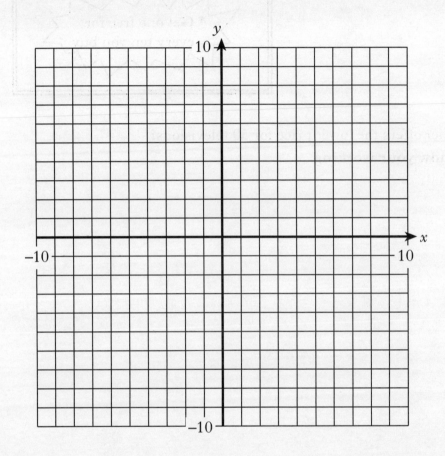

2

[Turn over

Marks

9. The manager of the Central Hotel is buying new televisions for each of the hotel's 50 bedrooms. Two suppliers offer him the following deals.

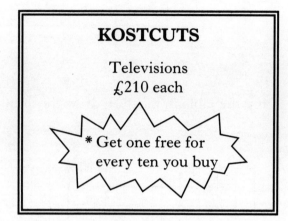

ELECTRO

Televisions
£199·99 each

KOSTCUTS

Televisions
£210 each

* Get one free for
every ten you buy

Which supplier offers the lower price for 50 televisions?

You must show your working.

4

Marks

10. Use the formula below to find the value of D when $b = 3$ and $k = 7$.

$$D = \sqrt{b^2 + k}$$

$D = \sqrt{3^2 + 7}$

$D = \sqrt{9 + 7}$

$D = \sqrt{16}$

$D = \pm 4 \times 4 = 4$

3

11. (*a*) Find $7 - (-2)$.

$7 - -2$

$7 + 2$

9

1

(*b*) Find $-24 \div (-3)$.

-8

1

[*END OF QUESTION PAPER*]

ADDITIONAL SPACE FOR ANSWERS

FOR OFFICIAL USE

Total mark

X056/103

NATIONAL
QUALIFICATIONS
2001

THURSDAY, 17 MAY
9.55 AM – 10.50 AM

MATHEMATICS
INTERMEDIATE 1
Units 1, 2 and 3
Paper 2

Fill in these boxes and read what is printed below.

Full name of centre

Town

Forename(s)

Surname

Date of birth
Day Month Year   Scottish candidate number   Number of seat

1 **You may use a calculator.**

2 Write your working and answers in the spaces provided. Additional space is provided at the end of this question-answer book for use if required. If you use this space, write clearly the number of the question involved.

3 Full credit will be given only where the solution contains appropriate working.

4 Before leaving the examination room you must give this book to the invigilator. If you do not you may lose all the marks for this paper.

SCOTTISH
QUALIFICATIONS
AUTHORITY

FORMULAE LIST

Circumference of a circle: $C = \pi d$
Area of a circle: $A = \pi r^2$

Theorem of Pythagoras:

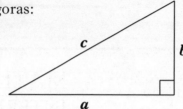 $a^2 + b^2 = c^2$

Trigonometric ratios
in a right angled
triangle:

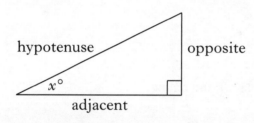 $\tan x^\circ = \dfrac{\text{opposite}}{\text{adjacent}}$

$\sin x^\circ = \dfrac{\text{opposite}}{\text{hypotenuse}}$

$\cos x^\circ = \dfrac{\text{adjacent}}{\text{hypotenuse}}$

DO NOT
WRITE IN
THIS
MARGIN

Marks

ALL questions should be attempted.

1.

Volume of pyramid = $\frac{1}{3}$ of (area of base × height)

(a) Use the formula above to work out the volume of this square-based pyramid.

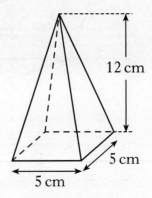

12 cm

5 cm

5 cm

3

(b) This cuboid has the same volume as the pyramid shown above.
Find the length of the cuboid.

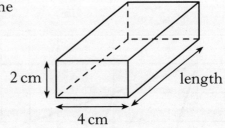

2 cm

4 cm

length

2

[Turn over

Marks

2. (*a*) Write down the coordinates of the point A marked on this diagram.

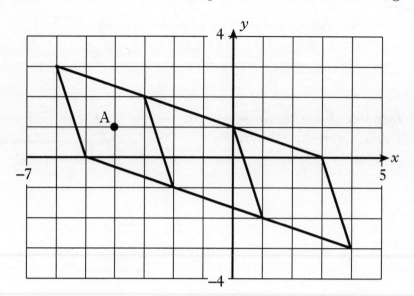

1

(*b*) The pattern of parallelograms continues.

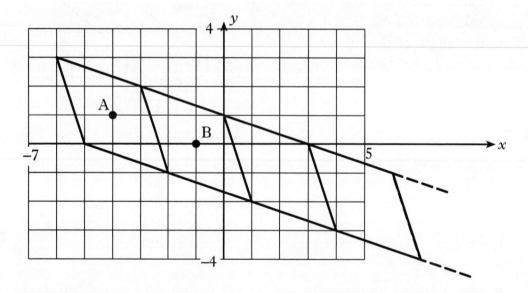

A is the centre of the first parallelogram.

B is the centre of the second parallelogram.

Find the coordinates of the centre of the sixth parallelogram.

2

Marks

3. A group of swimmers record

  • the number of lengths they swim in each training session
  • their personal best time (in seconds) for swimming 100 metres in competition.

The scattergraph shows the results.

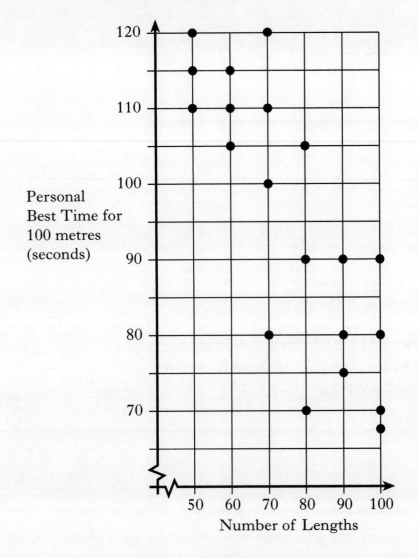

(a) Draw a line of best fit through the points on the graph.   1

(b) Use the graph to estimate the personal best time of a swimmer who swims 75 lengths in each training session.

1

[Turn over

Marks

4. Solve algebraically the inequality

$$2x + 3 > 10.$$

2

5. A compact disc can store 1.44×10^6 bytes of information.
How many bytes of information can 25 of these discs store?
Write your answer in standard form.

3

Marks

6. Andrea leaves home in Perth at 7 am and drives 40 miles to Edinburgh Airport where she then catches a flight to Dublin. Her journey is shown on the graph below.

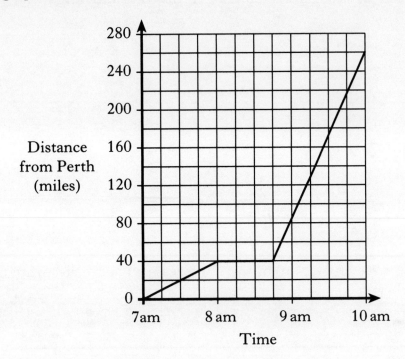

(a) How long does she spend waiting at Edinburgh Airport?

1

(b) Calculate the average speed of her flight from Edinburgh to Dublin.

4

[Turn over

Marks

7. Walter is a double glazing salesman.

   Each month he earns £500 **plus** 5% commission on all his sales.

   Calculate the value of his sales in a month when his **total earnings** were £1900.

3

8. The weights (to the nearest kilogram) of the 11 players in a hockey team are shown on the scale below.

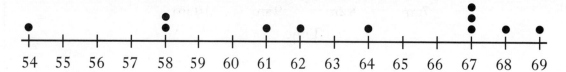

54   55   56   57   58   59   60   61   62   63   64   65   66   67   68   69

   (a) What percentage of the team weighs less than 60 kg?

   Give your answer correct to 1 decimal place.

4

   (b) Write down the median weight of the team.

1

   (c) If another player is added to the scale the new median is 65 kg. What is the weight of this player?

   Explain your answer.

2

Marks

9. The box office takings at cinemas in the UK and the USA from showing "The Spartans" are shown below.

    ### "THE SPARTANS"
    Box Office Takings

UK	£10 230 000
USA	$15 800 000

    Exchange Rate: £1 = $1·52

    Change the box office takings in the USA to pounds sterling.

    Give your answer to the nearest thousand pounds.

    3

10. A bypass is being built to reduce the traffic passing through Steevley as shown in the diagram.

    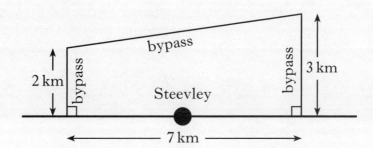

    Calculate the total length of the bypass.

    Do not use a scale drawing.

    4

Page nine

Marks

11. This sign is in the shape of a rectangle and a semi-circle.

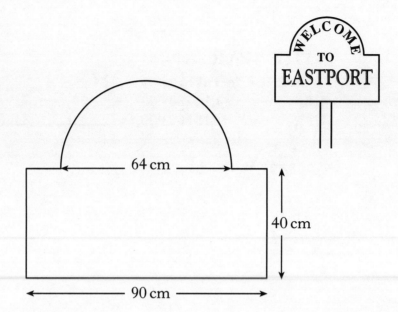

Calculate the area of the sign.

Give your answer to the nearest square centimetre.

5

Marks

12. The towers of a bridge are 200 metres apart.

Steel cables of length 49 metres are used to support the bridge at both ends.

The cables make an angle of 38° with the bridge.

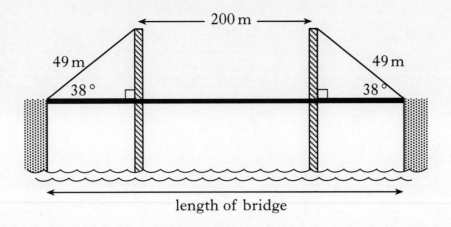

length of bridge

Find the total length of the bridge.

4

[*END OF QUESTION PAPER*]

DO NOT
WRITE I
THIS
MARGIN

ADDITIONAL SPACE FOR ANSWERS

INTERMEDIATE 1 2002

FOR OFFICIAL USE

Total mark

X100/101

NATIONAL
QUALIFICATIONS
2002

MONDAY, 27 MAY
1.00 PM – 1.35 PM

MATHEMATICS
INTERMEDIATE 1
Units 1, 2 and 3
Paper 1
(Non-calculator)

Fill in these boxes and read what is printed below.

Full name of centre

Town

Forename(s)

Surname

Date of birth
Day   Month   Year

Scottish candidate number

Number of seat

1   You may **NOT** use a calculator.

2   Write your working and answers in the spaces provided. Additional space is provided at the end of this question-answer book for use if required. If you use this space, write clearly the number of the question involved.

3   Full credit will be given only where the solution contains appropriate working.

4   Before leaving the examination room you must give this book to the invigilator. If you do not you may lose all the marks for this paper.

SCOTTISH
QUALIFICATIONS
AUTHORITY

FORMULAE LIST

Circumference of a circle: $C = \pi d$

Area of a circle: $A = \pi r^2$

Theorem of Pythagoras:

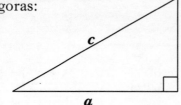

$a^2 + b^2 = c^2$

Trigonometric ratios
in a right angled
triangle:

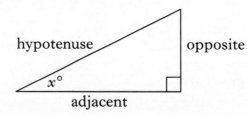

$$\tan x° = \frac{\text{opposite}}{\text{adjacent}}$$

$$\sin x° = \frac{\text{opposite}}{\text{hypotenuse}}$$

$$\cos x° = \frac{\text{adjacent}}{\text{hypotenuse}}$$

DO NOT WRITE IN THIS MARGIN

Marks

ALL questions should be attempted.

1. (*a*) Find $5 \cdot 22 \div 9$.

1

(*b*) Find $\frac{2}{5}$ of £80.

1

2. Find the volume of this cuboid.

12 cm

6 cm   7 cm

2

[Turn over

Marks

3. The graph shows the amount of full cream and semi-skimmed milk sold by a supermarket from 1990 to 2001.

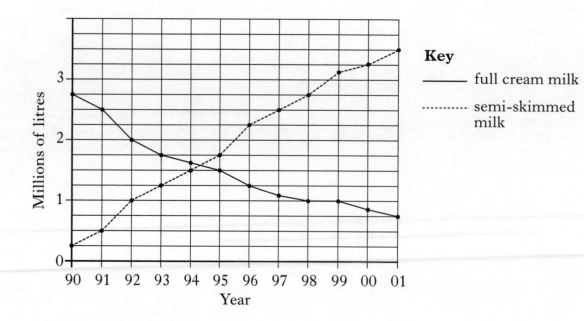

(a) How much semi-skimmed milk was sold in 1991?

1

(b) Describe the trend in sales of **both** kinds of milk.

1

Marks

4. This information appears on a box of chocolates.

Nutritional Information

per 100 grams

Energy	489 kJ
Protein	6·28 g
Carbohydrate	57·1 g
Fat	25·6 g

How much fat is in 300 grams of the chocolates?

2

[Turn over

Marks

5. Geeta is buying a new car. Her local garage has the following special offer on new cars.

SPECIAL OFFER on new cars **3** ITEMS FREE

Choose any THREE of these items up to a maximum value of £850

CD player	£150
Air Conditioning	£300
One year's Insurance	£400
Central Locking	£200
Electric Sunroof	£350

(a) One combination of items is shown in the table below.

CD player	Air Conditioning	One year's Insurance	Central Locking	Electric Sunroof	Total Value
✓		✓	✓		£750

Complete the table to show **all** the possible combinations of items available under this special offer.

3

(b) Geeta wants all five of these items.

She is willing to pay for the extra two items.

What is the least amount she must pay?

2

Marks

6. Solve algebraically the equation

$$5y + 7 = 19 - y.$$

3

7. (*a*) Complete the table below for $y = \frac{1}{2}x + 1$.

x	–8	0	6
y			

2

(*b*) Draw the line $y = \frac{1}{2}x + 1$ on the grid.

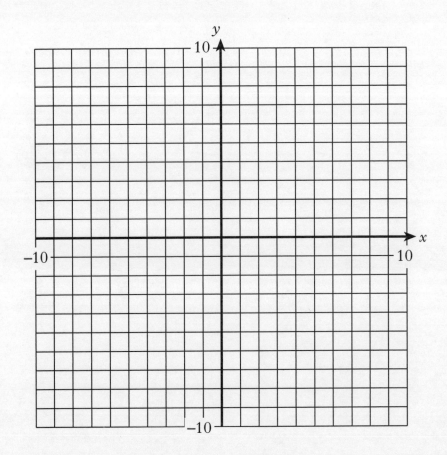

2

[Turn over

Marks

8. The full premium for John to insure his car last year was £480.

This year the premium has increased by one third.

John also receives a 20% discount on **this year's** premium.

How much will John pay to insure his car this year?

4

Marks

9. The attendances at six football matches are listed below.

    7000   10 000   64 000   11 000   10 000   12 000

    (a) Find the mean attendance.

2

    (b) Find the median attendance.

2

    (c) Which of the averages gives a truer picture of the above attendances
    — the mean or the median?
    Give a reason for your answer.

1

[Turn over for Question 10 on *Page ten*

Marks

10. Evaluate $3ab - c$ when $a = -1$, $b = 2$ and $c = -10$.

3

[*END OF QUESTION PAPER*]

FOR OFFICIAL USE

Total
mark

X100/103

NATIONAL	MONDAY, 27 MAY	MATHEMATICS
QUALIFICATIONS	1.55 PM – 2.50 PM	INTERMEDIATE 1
2002		Units 1, 2 and 3
		Paper 2

Fill in these boxes and read what is printed below.

Full name of centre

Town

Forename(s)

Surname

Date of birth
Day Month Year

Scottish candidate number

Number of seat

1 **You may use a calculator.**

2 Write your working and answers in the spaces provided. Additional space is provided at the end of this question-answer book for use if required. If you use this space, write clearly the number of the question involved.

3 Full credit will be given only where the solution contains appropriate working.

4 Before leaving the examination room you must give this book to the invigilator. If you do not you may lose all the marks for this paper.

SCOTTISH
QUALIFICATIONS
AUTHORITY

©

FORMULAE LIST

Circumference of a circle: $C = \pi d$

Area of a circle: $A = \pi r^2$

Theorem of Pythagoras:

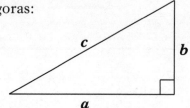

$a^2 + b^2 = c^2$

Trigonometric ratios
in a right angled
triangle:

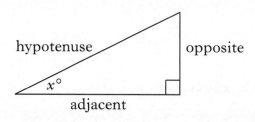

$$\tan x^\circ = \frac{\text{opposite}}{\text{adjacent}}$$

$$\sin x^\circ = \frac{\text{opposite}}{\text{hypotenuse}}$$

$$\cos x^\circ = \frac{\text{adjacent}}{\text{hypotenuse}}$$

Marks

ALL questions should be attempted.

1.   A letter is chosen at random from the letters of the word

MATHEMATICS.

What is the probability that the chosen letter is **M**?

1

2.   The wavelength of visible blue light is 0·000 072 centimetre.
Write this number in standard form.

2

[Turn over

Marks

3. The number of copies of "The Anglers Weekly" magazine sold by a newsagent was recorded for 16 weeks.

$$25 \quad 23 \quad 19 \quad 22 \quad 18 \quad 45 \quad 38 \quad 23$$
$$32 \quad 25 \quad 51 \quad 27 \quad 23 \quad 30 \quad 28 \quad 42$$

(a) Complete this stem and leaf diagram using the data above.

```
1 |
2 |
3 |
4 |
5 |
```

1|8 represents 18 magazines

2

(b) Find the mode for this data set.

1

Marks

4. Jane is going to Switzerland and wants to change £500 into Swiss francs. Two travel agents offer the following exchange rates.

TRAVELSUN	SOLLAIR
£1 = 2·46 Swiss francs	£1 = 2·50 Swiss francs
No commission	2% commission payable

(a) How many Swiss francs would Jane receive from Travelsun for £500?

1

(b) Which travel agent will give Jane more Swiss francs for her £500?
Show clearly all your working.

4

[Turn over

Marks

5. (*a*) Multiply out the brackets and simplify

$$5 + 4(2m - 3).$$

2

(*b*) Factorise $\quad 21 - 7t.$

2

Marks

6. Ali drove overnight 406 miles from Galashiels to Portsmouth to catch a ferry to France.

His average speed for the journey was 56 miles per hour.

He arrived in Portsmouth at 0630.

At what time did he leave Galashiels?

4

7. A group of students was asked how many times they had visited a cinema during the last month.

The results are shown in this frequency table.

Number of visits	Frequency	Visits × Frequency
0	104	
1	56	
2	44	
3	20	
4	10	
5	1	
	Total = 235	Total =

Complete the table above and find the mean number of visits.

Give your answer correct to 1 decimal place.

3

Marks

8. The circle shown below has centre (0,0).

The point (6,8) lies on the circle.

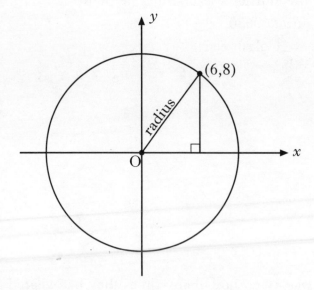

Work out the area of this circle.

4

9. Solve algebraically the inequality

$$4p + 3 < 27.$$

2

Marks

10. An art dealer paid £120 for an oil painting.

    He sold it for £150.

    Express the profit as a percentage of what he paid for the painting.

    4

11. The diagram shows the positions of three towns.

    Braley is 38 kilometres from Aldwich.

    Cannich is due east of Aldwich.

    Braley is 35 kilometres due south of Cannich.

    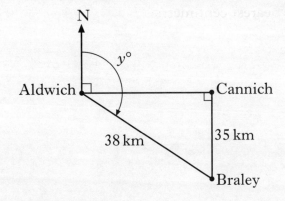

    Calculate $y°$, the bearing of Braley from Aldwich.

    Do not use a scale drawing.

    4

    [Turn over

Marks

12. This window blind is in the shape of a rectangle with four equal semi-circles at the bottom.

It has braid down the two sides and round the bottom.

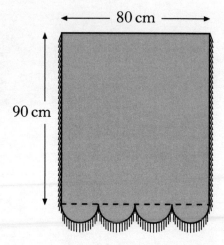

Calculate the total length of braid needed for this blind.

Give your answer to the nearest centimetre.

5

Marks

13. Body mass index is a measure of weight compared to height.

The body mass index, B, of a person who weighs w kilograms and whose height is h metres is given by the formula

$$B = \frac{w}{h^2}.$$

(a) Calculate the value of B for a person who weighs 70 kilograms and is 1·68 metres tall.

3

(b) Tom is 1·55 metres tall.
His body mass index is 25.
Find his weight.

2

[END OF QUESTION PAPER]

Page eleven

DO NOT
WRITE I
THIS
MARGIN

ADDITIONAL SPACE FOR ANSWERS

INTERMEDIATE 1 2003

FOR OFFICIAL USE

Total
mark

X100/101

NATIONAL
QUALIFICATIONS
2003

WEDNESDAY, 21 MAY
1.30 PM – 2.05 PM

MATHEMATICS
INTERMEDIATE 1
Units 1, 2 and 3
Paper 1
(Non-calculator)

Fill in these boxes and read what is printed below.

Full name of centre

Town

Forename(s)

Surname

Date of birth
Day   Month   Year   Scottish candidate number   Number of seat

1   **You may NOT use a calculator.**

2   Write your working and answers in the spaces provided. Additional space is provided at the end of this question-answer book for use if required. If you use this space, write clearly the number of the question involved.

3   Full credit will be given only where the solution contains appropriate working.

4   Before leaving the examination room you must give this book to the invigilator. If you do not you may lose all the marks for this paper.

SCOTTISH
QUALIFICATIONS
AUTHORITY

©

FORMULAE LIST

Circumference of a circle: $C = \pi d$
Area of a circle: $A = \pi r^2$

Theorem of Pythagoras:

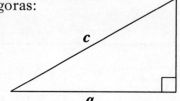

$a^2 + b^2 = c^2$

Trigonometric ratios
in a right angled
triangle:

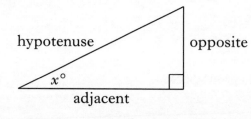

$$\tan x° = \frac{\text{opposite}}{\text{adjacent}}$$

$$\sin x° = \frac{\text{opposite}}{\text{hypotenuse}}$$

$$\cos x° = \frac{\text{adjacent}}{\text{hypotenuse}}$$

Marks

ALL questions should be attempted.

1. (*a*) Find $6.23 - 3.7$.

1

(*b*) Find 5% of £140.

1

(*c*) Find $-40 + 15$.

1

2. A rule used to calculate the cost in pounds of electricity is:

> Cost = 19 + (number of units used × 0·07)

Find the cost of 600 units of electricity.

2

[Turn over

Marks

3. (*a*) An inter-city coach left Aberdeen at 10.40 am and reached Inverness at 1.25 pm.

How long did the journey take?

1

(*b*) The average speed of the coach during the journey was 40 miles per hour.

Find the distance between Aberdeen and Inverness.

3

4. Solve algebraically the equation

$$8c + 3 = 31 + c.$$

3

Marks

5. Andy wants to make 150 copies of a music booklet.

8 sheets of paper are required for each booklet.

(*a*) Find the total number of sheets required.

1

Paper is sold in packets which contain 500 sheets.

(*b*) How many packets of paper will Andy need to buy?

2

6. Solve algebraically the inequality

$$9m - 2 > 70.$$

2

[Turn over

Marks

7. (*a*) Complete the table below for $y = 1 \cdot 5x - 1$.

x	-2	0	6
y			

2

(*b*) Draw the line $y = 1 \cdot 5x - 1$ on the grid.

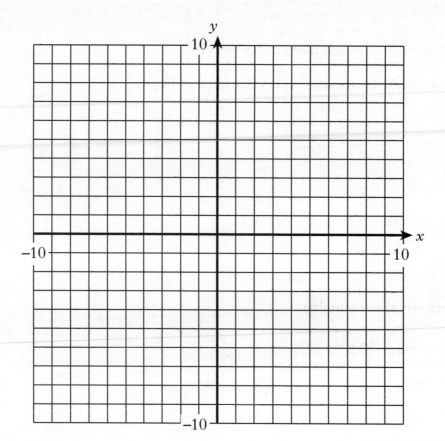

2

Marks

8. In a local election the number of votes for each of the four candidates is shown in the table below.

Candidate	Votes
Smith	380
Patel	240
Green	100
Jones	170

On the grid below, draw a bar graph to show this information.

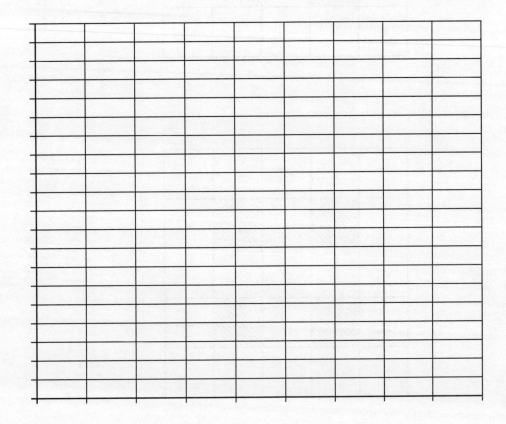

4

9. Five staff work in an office.

Three of them are female.

What percentage of the staff is female?

3

Marks

10. This is a multiplication square.

8	×	5	=	40
×		×		×
10	×	−2	=	−20
=		=		=
80	×	−10	=	−800

(a) Complete this multiplication square.

3	×	−7	=	
×		×		×
−1	×	5	=	
=		=		=
	×		=	

2

Marks

10. (continued)

(*b*) Complete this multiplication square.

−5	×		=	
×		×		×
	×		=	−12
=		=		=
	×	−8	=	−120

3

[*END OF QUESTION PAPER*]

ADDITIONAL SPACE FOR ANSWERS

FOR OFFICIAL USE

Total mark

X100/103

NATIONAL
QUALIFICATIONS
2003

WEDNESDAY, 21 MAY
2.25 PM – 3.20 PM

MATHEMATICS
INTERMEDIATE 1
Units 1, 2 and 3
Paper 2

Fill in these boxes and read what is printed below.

Full name of centre

Town

Forename(s)

Surname

Date of birth
Day Month Year

Scottish candidate number

Number of seat

1 **You may use a calculator.**

2 Write your working and answers in the spaces provided. Additional space is provided at the end of this question-answer book for use if required. If you use this space, write clearly the number of the question involved.

3 Full credit will be given only where the solution contains appropriate working.

4 Before leaving the examination room you must give this book to the invigilator. If you do not you may lose all the marks for this paper.

SCOTTISH
QUALIFICATIONS
AUTHORITY

©

FORMULAE LIST

Circumference of a circle: $\qquad C = \pi d$

Area of a circle: $\qquad A = \pi r^2$

Theorem of Pythagoras:

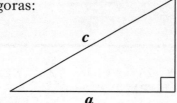

$$a^2 + b^2 = c^2$$

Trigonometric ratios
in a right angled
triangle:

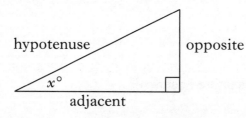

$$\tan x° = \frac{\text{opposite}}{\text{adjacent}}$$

$$\sin x° = \frac{\text{opposite}}{\text{hypotenuse}}$$

$$\cos x° = \frac{\text{adjacent}}{\text{hypotenuse}}$$

Marks

ALL questions should be attempted.

1. A day in December is chosen at random for a youth club outing.

   Find the probability that a **Saturday** is chosen.

DECEMBER

Mon	Tue	Wed	Thu	Fri	Sat	Sun
1	2	3	4	5	6	7
8	9	10	11	12	13	14
15	16	17	18	19	20	21
22	23	24	25	26	27	28
29	30	31				

1

2. A common cold virus is 5×10^{-4} millimetres long.

   Write this number in full.

2

[Turn over

Marks

3. (*a*) Multiply out the brackets and simplify

$$5(a + 2b) - 3b.$$

2

(*b*) Factorise $6n + 30$.

2

           Page four

Marks

4. The income of each employee in a company is shown in this frequency table.

Income £	Frequency	Income × Frequency
10 000	2	
12 000	3	
14 000	5	
16 000	8	
18 000	7	
	Total = 25	Total =

(a) Write down the modal income.

1

(b) Complete the table above and find the mean income.

3

[Turn over

Marks

5. A room in the Hotel Royale in Paris costs 130 euros per night.
The exchange rate is 1·58 euros to the pound.

(*a*) Find the cost of the hotel room per night in pounds and pence.

3

Mr and Mrs McQueen are going to Paris.
Their return flights cost £59 each.

(*b*) Find the total cost of their flights and a 3 night stay at the Hotel Royale in pounds and pence.

2

Marks

6. The population of Scotland in 2001 was 5 062 000.

The pie chart shows the age distribution of the population in 2001.

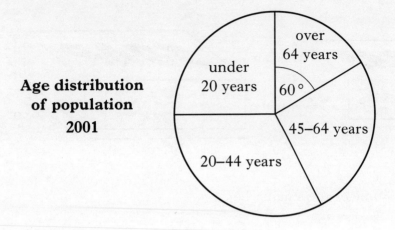

**Age distribution
of population
2001**

(*a*) How many people were aged over 64 years?

Give your answer to the nearest thousand.

3

(*b*) The pie chart below shows the age distribution of the population of Scotland in 1901.

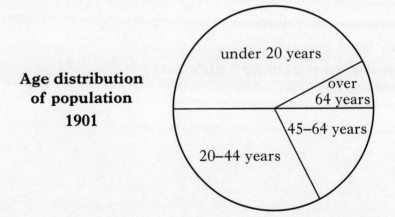

**Age distribution
of population
1901**

Describe the differences in the age distributions of the population of Scotland in 1901 and 2001.

2

Marks

7. The diagram below shows two bars of soap.
    Each bar is in the shape of a cuboid.

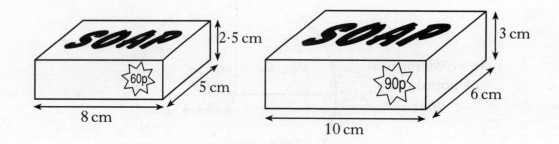

2·5 cm

5 cm

8 cm

3 cm

6 cm

10 cm

(a) Find the volume of the smaller bar.

1

(b) The smaller bar costs 60 pence.
     Find the cost per cubic centimetre of the smaller bar.

1

(c) The larger bar costs 90 pence.
     Which bar of soap gives better value for money?
     Explain clearly the reason for your answer.

3

Marks

8. Use the formula below to find the value of R when $P = 180$, $M = 7 \cdot 5$ and $N = 5$.

$$R = \frac{P}{MN}$$

3

9. The diagram shows the front view of a garage.

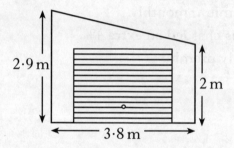

Calculate the length of the sloping edge of the roof.
Do not use a scale drawing.

3

[Turn over

DO NOT
WRITE IN
THIS
MARGIN

Marks

10. Gail wants to insure her computer for £2400.

The insurance company charges an annual premium of £1·25 for each £100 insured.

(*a*) Calculate the annual premium.

2

(*b*) Gail can pay her premium monthly.

If she does this she is charged an extra 4%.

Calculate the monthly premium.

3

Marks

11. A television mast is supported by wires.

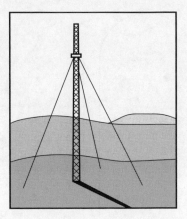

The diagram below shows one of the wires which is 80 metres long. The wire is attached to the mast 20 metres from the top and makes an angle of 59° with the ground.

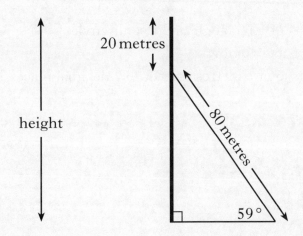

Calculate the height of the mast.

Give your answer to the nearest metre.

Do not use a scale drawing.

5

[Turn over for Question 12 on *Page twelve*

DO NOT
WRITE IN
THIS
MARGIN

Marks

12. The diagram below shows a window.

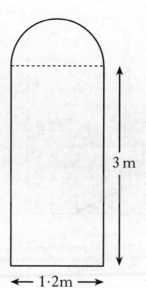

3 m

← 1·2m →

The window consists of a rectangle and a semi-circle.

Calculate the area of the window.

Give your answer in square metres correct to 2 decimal places.

5

[END OF QUESTION PAPER]

FOR OFFICIAL USE

Total
mark

X100/101

NATIONAL
QUALIFICATIONS
2004

FRIDAY, 21 MAY
1.00 PM – 1.35 PM

MATHEMATICS
INTERMEDIATE 1
Units 1, 2 and 3
Paper 1
(Non-calculator)

Fill in these boxes and read what is printed below.

Full name of centre

Town

Forename(s)

Surname

Date of birth
Day Month Year   Scottish candidate number   Number of seat

1 **You may NOT use a calculator.**

2 Write your working and answers in the spaces provided. Additional space is provided at the end of this question-answer book for use if required. If you use this space, write clearly the number of the question involved.

3 Full credit will be given only where the solution contains appropriate working.

4 Before leaving the examination room you must give this book to the invigilator. If you do not you may lose all the marks for this paper.

SCOTTISH
QUALIFICATIONS
AUTHORITY

©

FORMULAE LIST

Circumference of a circle: $C = \pi d$

Area of a circle: $A = \pi r^2$

Theorem of Pythagoras:

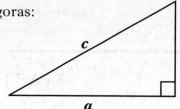

$$a^2 + b^2 = c^2$$

Trigonometric ratios
in a right angled
triangle:

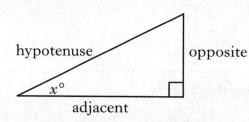

$$\tan x^\circ = \frac{\text{opposite}}{\text{adjacent}}$$

$$\sin x^\circ = \frac{\text{opposite}}{\text{hypotenuse}}$$

$$\cos x^\circ = \frac{\text{adjacent}}{\text{hypotenuse}}$$

Marks

ALL questions should be attempted.

1. Work out the answers to the following.

   (a) 30% of £230

   1

   (b) $\dfrac{4}{7}$ of 105

   1

   (c) 380 − 20 × 9

   1

2. A cooker can be bought by paying a deposit of £59 followed by 12 instalments of £45.

   Calculate the total price of the cooker.

   2

[Turn over

Marks

3. Calculate the volume of this cuboid.

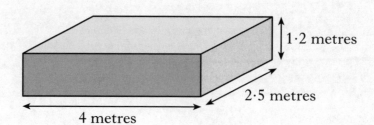

1·2 metres

2·5 metres

4 metres

2

4. The temperatures, in degrees Celsius, at noon for the first ten days in January at Invergow were:

$$-3 \quad 0 \quad -2 \quad 2 \quad -1 \quad -4 \quad -5 \quad -3 \quad 1 \quad 3.$$

Calculate

(*a*) the median temperature;

2

(*b*) the range.

2

Marks

4. (continued)

(*c*) The corresponding values of the median and the range for Abergrange
are 2 °C and 5 °C respectively.

Make **two** comments comparing the temperatures in Invergow and
Abergrange.

2

5. Solve algebraically the equation

$$11 + 5x = 2x + 29.$$

$$5x = 2x + 29 + 11$$
$$5x = 2x + 18$$
$$5x - 2x = 18$$
$$3x = 18$$
$$x = \frac{18}{3}$$
$$x = 6$$

3

[Turn over

Marks

6. A shop sells artificial flowers.
The prices of individual flowers are shown below.

Variety	Price
Carnation	£2
Daffodil	£3·50
Lily	£4
Iris	£3
Rose	£4·50

Zara wants to • buy 3 flowers

      • choose 3 different varieties

      • spend a **minimum** of £10.

One combination of flowers that Zara can buy is shown in the table below.

Carnation	Daffodil	Lily	Iris	Rose	Total Price
		✓	✓	✓	£11·50

Complete the table to show **all** the possible combinations that Zara can buy.   **3**

Marks

7. An Internet provider has a customer helpline.
The length of each telephone call to the helpline was recorded one day.
The results are shown in the frequency table below.

Length of call (to nearest minute)	Frequency	Length of call × Frequency
1	15	15
2	40	80
3	26	78
4	29	116
5	49	
6	41	
	Total = 200	Total =

(*a*) Complete the table above and find the mean length of call.

3

(*b*) Write down the modal length of call.

1

[Turn over

Marks

8. (*a*) Complete the table below for $y = 3 - x$.

x	-2	2	7
y			

2

(*b*) Draw the line $y = 3 - x$ on the grid.

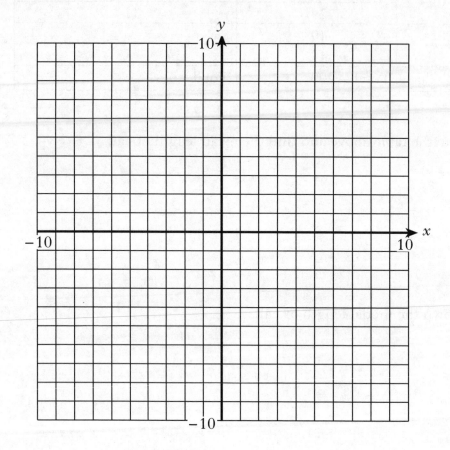

2

Marks

9. One billion is 1000 million.

A country borrows 2×10^{10} dollars.

How many billions of dollars is this?

3

10. Evaluate $\dfrac{2xy}{z}$ when $x = -5$, $y = 6$ and $z = -4$.

$$\frac{2(-5)(6)}{-4}$$

$$= \frac{-10(6)}{4}$$

$$\frac{-60}{-4}$$

$$15$$

$$4\overline{)60} = 15$$

3

[END OF QUESTION PAPER]

ADDITIONAL SPACE FOR ANSWERS

FOR OFFICIAL USE

Total mark

X100/103

NATIONAL
QUALIFICATIONS
2004

FRIDAY, 21 MAY
1.55 PM – 2.50 PM

MATHEMATICS
INTERMEDIATE 1
Units 1, 2 and 3
Paper 2

Fill in these boxes and read what is printed below.

Full name of centre

Town

Forename(s)

Surname

Date of birth

Day Month Year   Scottish candidate number   Number of seat

1   **You may use a calculator.**

2   Write your working and answers in the spaces provided. Additional space is provided at the end of this question-answer book for use if required. If you use this space, write clearly the number of the question involved.

3   Full credit will be given only where the solution contains appropriate working.

4   Before leaving the examination room you must give this book to the invigilator. If you do not you may lose all the marks for this paper.

SCOTTISH
QUALIFICATIONS
AUTHORITY

FORMULAE LIST

Circumference of a circle: $\qquad C = \pi d$

Area of a circle: $\qquad A = \pi r^2$

Theorem of Pythagoras:

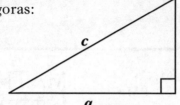

$$a^2 + b^2 = c^2$$

Trigonometric ratios
in a right angled
triangle:

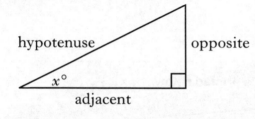

$$\tan x^\circ = \frac{\text{opposite}}{\text{adjacent}}$$

$$\sin x^\circ = \frac{\text{opposite}}{\text{hypotenuse}}$$

$$\cos x^\circ = \frac{\text{adjacent}}{\text{hypotenuse}}$$

Marks

ALL questions should be attempted.

1. 2000 tickets are sold for a raffle in which the star prize is a television.
Kirsty buys 10 tickets for the raffle.
What is the probability that she wins the star prize?

1

2. (*a*) On the grid below, plot the points A(–3, 4), B(2, 4) and C(6, –5).

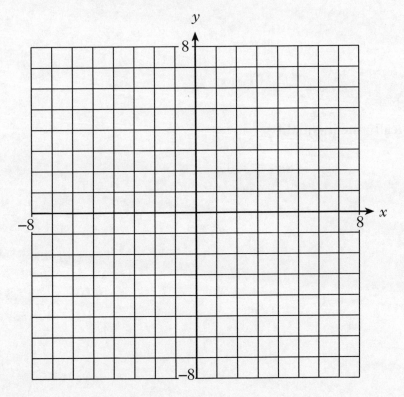

2

(*b*) Plot the point D so that shape ABCD is a kite.
Write down the coordinates of point D.

2

[**Turn over**

Marks

3. An overnight train left London at 2040 and reached Inverness at 0810 the next day.

The distance travelled by the train was 552 miles.

Calculate the average speed of the train.

3

4. Solve algebraically the inequality

$$8n - 3 < 37.$$

2

Marks

5. The scattergraph shows the age and mileage of cars in a garage.

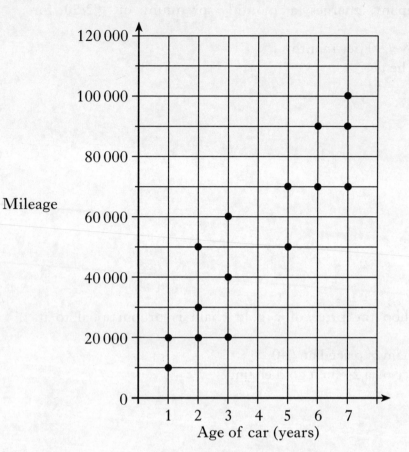

(*a*) Draw a line of best fit through the points on the graph.

1

(*b*) Use your line of best fit to estimate the mileage of a 4 year old car.

1

6. (*a*) Multiply out the brackets and simplify

$$2(4 - t) + 5t.$$

2

(*b*) Factorise $10y - 35$.

2

Page five

[Turn over

Marks

7. Ryan wants to take out a life insurance policy.
    The insurance company charges a monthly premium of £2·50 for each £1000 of cover.
    Ryan can afford to pay £90 per month.
    How much cover can he get?

2

8. (a) In a jewellery shop the price of a gold chain is proportional to its length.
    A 16 inch gold chain is priced at £40.
    Calculate the price of a 24 inch gold chain.

2

    (b) The gold chains are displayed diagonally on a **square** board of side 20 inches.
    The longest chain stretches from corner to corner.
    Calculate the length of the longest chain.
    Do not use a scale drawing.

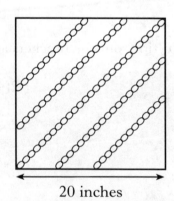

20 inches

3

Marks

9. Andy buys a bottle of aftershave in Spain for 38·50 euros.
    The same bottle of aftershave costs £25·99 in Scotland.
    The exchange rate is £1 = 1·52 euros.
    Does he save money by buying the aftershave in Spain?
    Explain your answer.

3

10. The front of the tent shown below is an isosceles triangle.

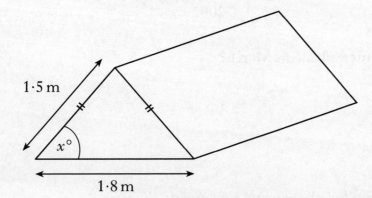

1·5 m

$x°$

1·8 m

The size of the angle between the side and the bottom of the tent is $x°$.
Calculate x.

4

Marks

11. The graph below shows how the rate of interest for a savings account with the Clydeside Bank changed during 2002.

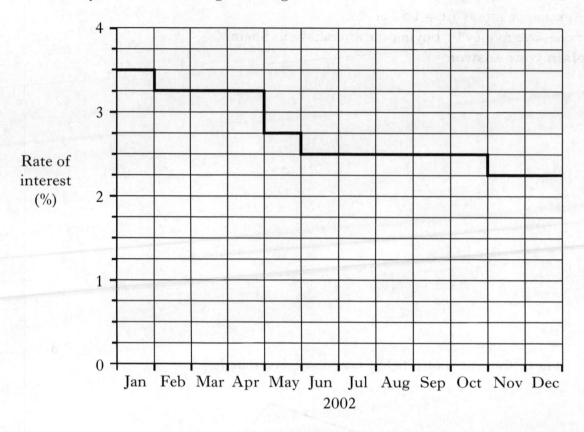

(*a*) What was the interest rate in March?

1

(*b*) Describe the trend of the interest rate during the year.

1

(*c*) In June £1400 was invested in this account.
How much interest was due after 3 months?

4

Marks

12. The minimum velocity v metres per second, allowed at the top of a loop in a roller coaster, is given by the formula

$$v = \sqrt{gr}$$

where r metres is the radius of the loop.

Calculate the value of v when $g = 9{\cdot}81$ and $r = 9$.

3

13. 40 people were asked whether they preferred tea or coffee.

18 of them said they preferred coffee.

What percentage said they preferred coffee?

3

[Turn over

Marks

14. The diagram below shows a rectangular door with a window.

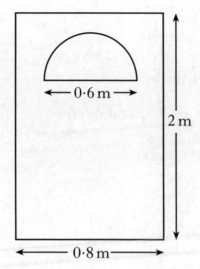

The window is in the shape of a semi-circle and is made of glass.

The rest of the door is made of wood.

Calculate the area of the wooden part of the door.

Give your answer in square metres correct to two decimal places.

5

[END OF QUESTION PAPER]

[BLANK PAGE]

[BLANK PAGE]

[BLANK PAGE]

[BLANK PAGE]

[BLANK PAGE]

[BLANK PAGE]